Purple

by Liza Charlesworth

ISBN: 978-1-338-78289-9
Illustrated by John Lund
Copyright © 2021 by Liza Charlesworth. All rights reserved.
Published by Scholastic Inc., 557 Broadway, New York, NY 10012

10 9 8 7 6 5 4 3 2 1   68   21 22 23 24 25 26 27/0

Printed in Jiaxing, China. First printing, June 2021.

Purple Pen is an artist!
She knows **how**
to draw dogs.

Purple Pen is an artist!
She knows **how**
to draw dinosaurs.

Purple Pen is an artist!
She knows **how**
to draw snowmen.

Purple Pen is an artist!
She knows **how**
to draw unicorns.

Purple Pen is an artist!
She knows **how**
to draw monsters.

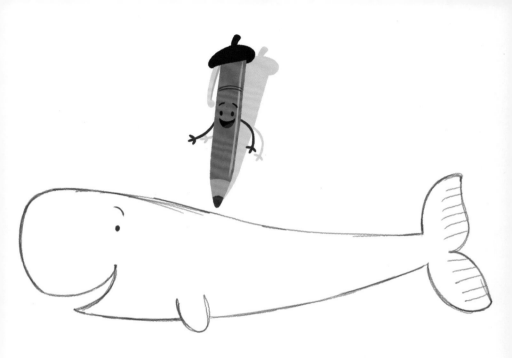

Purple Pen is an artist!
She knows **how**
to draw whales.

Purple Pen is an artist!
She knows **how**
to draw pals.